www.united-pc.eu

Martyn Mulvey

Cockerpoo Capers:

Lula's Blog

Feawell Cottage – Orkney

.

The Journey

25/11 – Travel to Stirling

26/11 – Stirling to Inverness

27/11 – Inverness – John O Groats – Gills Bay – Orkney

28/11 - 6/12 Feawell Cottage Orkney

6/12 – Orkney – Ullapool

7/12 – Ullapool – Loch Ness – Fort William

8/12 – Fort William – Carlisle

9/12 – Carlisle – Home

Hope you enjoy

Love Lula xx

25/11/19 - Off to Stirling

Steady start – left home all excited for a long drive to Stirling, bit of a day but slept through most of it, Dad did all of the driving – I did offer, but you know what he's like.

No photo's today, apparently he can't multi-task – driving and taking photo's at the same time are beyond him – he makes the excuse it's not legal or safe.

Anyway we've driven for about 6 hrs, he had a takeaway, I had my biscuits and we settled down for an early night.

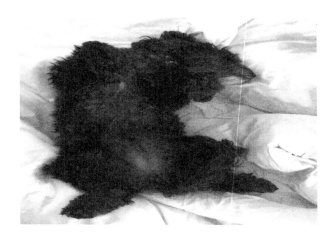

Cream Crackered

26/11/19 Stirling to Inverness

Brekkie – done.

Post Brekkie Power Nap – done.

Out for a little Haggis Hunting before we set off to explore Stirling.

Apparently haggis hunting will let me stretch my legs before we get in the car – **I was happy enough stretching in bed!**

We're off to a few places today, not sure what they all are but we're doing Bannockburn, Stirling Castle, the William Wallace monument and then driving up to Inverness.

Bannockburn

First proper visit of the day – Site of a battle, some bloke called Bob (Robert) kicked England's backside in a fight – mind you he was a big lad, look at the photo's.

Great place though – I had a good sniff and run around here.

Next : off to see Stirling Castle.

Stirling Castle

OOPs! This is actually an old kennel where all the bad blokes were kept – they call it a jail.

TBH we thought this was the castle at first, bit of a blonde moment from Dad.

The real Stirling Castle

Really nice place – but they wouldn't let me in any further.

The Big Spiky Thing

We're still in Stirling and getting closer to the Spiky Thing.

Its massive, and half way up a mountain, not sure what's happened here - it was tiny when we saw it from the castle.

Bad News – this is as close as we can get with the car, we're catching a horse called Shank's pony to the top, suppose it'll make a change from driving.

Getting closer – and I now know what Shank's pony is.

We've had to walk it !!!

It felt like miles, and it's all up hill, what a climb for my little legs! But wow so worth it.

It's the **William Wallace Monument** – another guy that gave the English a good kicking, not surprising if you see the size of his sword.

What a fabulous building this is, and the views are stunning, have a look at the next photo, if you ever come to Stirling you have to visit here it's great.

Right, time to go – thankfully it's all downhill back to the car. I'll have a power nap while he drives to Inverness.

Made a new friend

We've stopped for a quick 'comfort' break – i.e. he needed a wee, took the chance to say hello to the locals – nice guy this one, a little quiet but he was ok.

A chap took the photo - I had the wriggle bum and wouldn't sit still.

Inverness

We've arrived safe and sound in Inverness. Too dark for photo's, lovely ladies behind reception made such a fuss.

I'm fed, watered, and walked. The Scottish air and mountaineering up to the monument have done me in.

Night, Night, I'm off to bed.

Love from Lula x
(and of course Love from Dad x)

27/11 Day 3 Inverness - John O Groat's – Gills Bay - Orkney

Morning everybody – we're off. It's cold, raining and very windy, he's dragged me out of bed, there's nothing exciting in the car park worth taking a picture of.

We've a couple of hours drive to John 'O' Groats which is the traditional furthest northerly point of Britain (that's actually Dunnett Head – but Dad says we'll pass that later in the week).

Time for a power nap in the car.

John 'O' Groats

We've arrived. It's blowing an absolute gale, there's not a lot here, and what is here is only partly open, but hey ho its quiet and parking is easy even for Dad.

I didn't want to share this photo – **just look at the coat !!!**

Think you can tell I'm not happy!

When the lady who took the picture said 'Smile' - I thought "you're having a laugh", do you really want me to look like the clown from 'IT'?

John 'O' Groats done – Off to Gill's Bay.

Gill's Bay

We're here to catch something called a 'ferry' –
supposedly we've got to do that because I don't
swim, *I thought it might be my fault some how*,
the ferry will take us across the sea to Orkney.

We're in the queue – *I'm on ferry watch.*

Hoorah! - it's here, its massive – they had to back it in.

Dad says it's not that big, but it is to me - he seems to forget he's 10 times bigger than I am.

Bye Bye Scotland.

Stroma

This is **Stroma** – an island we pass on the
way, there's a lighthouse just to the left of the
lifeboat – Dad couldn't get a better picture of it
– **bit too technical for him.**

Ah Ah – Ahoy Orkney – it's in the distance, that's where we're going

Fortunately no sea sickness – *(then again I'd like to have seen him tackle that with nothing but a poo bag!! – LOL).*

Nearly there.

We've come outside to watch the docking, still very windy and rainy – this bench is soaking – *if I end up with piles he can get ready!*

Feawell Cottage

We've arrived – its dark, rainy, and windy, outside, the weather's too bad for photo's, we've met Ann and Eddie who own the place, they're great.

Eddie wants me to stay for good, *guess it was love at first sight – I've told him I'll think about it.*

The cottage is lovely – it's warm, dry, and cosy, we've unpacked, I'm fed, watered and chilled ready for bed.

Night all – Love Lula x
(and of course love from Dad x)

(He say's there's no signal to call whatever that means)

29

28/11/19 Feawell – First Day

We're sat on the doorstep. Dad's got his cup of tea and we're waiting for the sunrise. It's a little windy but the rains stopped, I think it's going to be good here.

Change of plan!

Dad's had his tea. I caught Eddie sneaking across the yard going to work – he's had the full facial – face, neck, ears – I think it set him up for the day.

Apparently, I need some exercise, *(I'm not so sure about that TBH)* so now we're having an early start. Ann's filled Dad in on how to get to the shore.

We're off even before the sun's showing, not sure I'll be keeping this up!

We go up the lane, turn left, go down two fields, follow the path down to the shore and then we can walk along it for miles.

I'm not too keen on that but it looks like we're going anyway.

Bonus – we pass over a field full of manure – lush, some really tasty bits, went down well with me but not grumpy Dad, hey ho he'll enjoy the licking later on – I've not even packed my toothbrush – *(Hee Hee).*

First Feawell Sunrise

Oh Wow!

I'm a dog but even I found this impressive.

We're at the shore.

It's great.

We've had a good walk, and I managed a spot of crabbing. Dad wouldn't come in - too cold apparently. He's getting soft in his old age - LOL

We've arrived back.

Dad has a cuppa, I'm just sat on his knee watching the sun, and enjoying the view.

The Standing Stones of Stennes

– first visit of the day.

Nice here – had a good run around, I had to sort out the 3 rams, they were a bit grumpy, nice picture of me and Dad I thought.

This last picture is called **The Watch Stone** – I don't know why it's called that – it doesn't tell the time, probably needs a new battery, it is about 3000 years old after all.

Next stop – the **Ness of Brodger**

Ness of Brodger

Hmmm – looks like a tarpaulin covered in old tyres to me, I didn't know they had cars in Neolithic times.

Ah - Archaeologists are still digging this site out according to Dad, they only work in the summer months and cover the place up to protect it in the winter.

Not a good time to visit this one – nothing to see really, would be better when the site's open!

Perhaps they'd let me help them dig, I'm sure they wouldn't miss the odd bone or two.

The Ring of Brodger

This site is huge – I can't imagine how they did this without cranes or bulldozers – it's great.

This is another 3,000 year old site – its massive. We walked all around it.

Dad had to join me in the trench when I called for a quick wee – *(probably shouldn't have told you that)*.

Short break from history for a minute – we arrived at Skara Brae and rainbows were out.

The piccies don't do them justice – they were 2, arced right over the building – bit embarrassing really, we went running up a path in the rain to try and get a picture but it didn't come out right.

Dad and techie stuff – not a match made in heaven!

The Neolithic Village of Skara Brae

What a place, its 3000 years old, a great place to visit.

You walk down a path which has stones laid saying when memorable things were happening in the world, they're laid at a distance equal to the time they happened from the gate most recent nearest to the gate, e.g. **Fall of Rome** AD 476, and further away **Building of the Pyramids of Gaza** 2500 BC.

This little village is farthest from the gate, its older than any of them – what a great way of showing how old it is.

There were 8 houses built into a little village – reminded me of the Shire from the Hobbit.

These piccies show a reconstruction of one of the houses – *I'm thinking of moving in here.*

43

Also met a guide called Glyn here – really nice chap, told us loads about the place.

I thought he'd earned the treatment so he had to have the full works, he loved most of it. I think the crotch sniff made him very nervous, for some reason he didn't seem too impressed by that bit – can't think why.

This was the doorway to the reconstructed house – thought I'd have a quick pose to see how I looked before I decide whether to move in permanently or not.

Next stop and last visit of the day – **Birsay Island.**

Birsay Island

This is good – it's a headland that's cut off at high tide – at low tide you can walk across to the island, managed to talk Dad out of that, we've done miles today in wind, rain, sunshine, then more wind, more rain and more sunshine already.

Right – That's enough sight seeing for today – its time to head home.

We're back.

I'm in my chair, warm, fed, watered and even managed a late night cuddle with Eddie before turning in – he had to have his bedtime wash before I let him go.

That's all for today folks – catch up tomorrow.

Loads of love Lula xx
P.S. Love from Dad too, though he's a bit grumpy, he's made some scones and burnt them – LOL xx

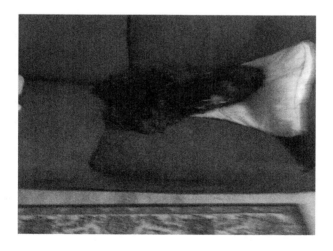

Friday 29/11/19

We're having a steady day today, this was the view first thing this morning, there's a scattering of snow on the hills in the distance that's how cold it was yesterday and last night.

We're having a later start.

Breakfast - full English (*or should it be Scottish*) for Dad, just biscuits for me – *there's something not quite right about that!*

Breakfast done, we're off to see the Italian Chapel.

The Italian Chapel

This is brilliant, Italian prisoners of war built it out of a Nissen hut, it's fabulous.

These are the outside photo's, really good. *(Especially the 2 bulls fighting in the field next door – LOL).*

Wait for the next page – the prisoners painted everything, it brilliant, the tiles on the wall are actually painted, not real tiles at all, you wouldn't know unless you were told.

It's a great place to visit and you can read the full story whilst you're there, if you ever go to Orkney it's another 'must see' place.

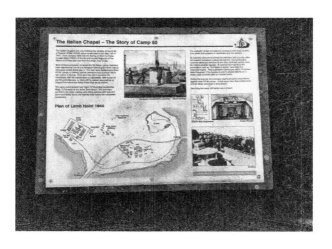

The Italian Chapel – The Story of Camp 60

Plan of Lamb Holm 1944

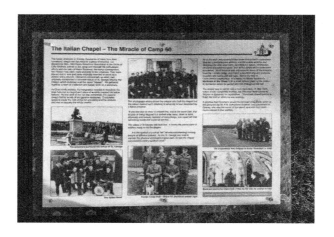

The Italian Chapel – The Miracle of Camp 60

This is the inside. Just a note – the head of Christ is on the outside and is carved out of concrete - how good is that.

Told you it was stunning

Next Visit - Tomb of the Eagles

We've driven for ½ hr which was ok, went through rush hour on Orkney – which actually means we saw another car in the distance – LOL, we drove down a couple of cart tracks, (Orkney B roads), only to find that the tomb was closed until March. Dad thought that was a bit too long to wait so we've decided to head back.

Kirkwall – We've stopped at the small city of Kirkwall for a mooch around, not very big as cities go but it's nice enough. I managed to sniff every paving stone and building corner in the place so it took us a little longer than normal.

I had to have a grump at a labrador trying to muscle in on Dads' hot chocolate – soon sorted him out – Orkney pussy!

Got home and gave Eddie his evening wash – he gave Dad a great big crab which was still moving! It tried to nip Dad – *big big mistake !!*

Dad sorted it, he plonked it into a pan of boiling water and then eat it! You don't want to get on the wrong side of Dad, he's got a bit of a vicious streak at times.

I thought eating the thing was a bit harsh though! I'm on best behaviour for the rest of the night !!!!

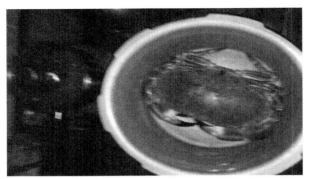

Crabby before

Crabby after

We're off to visit Dad's mate tomorrow, an old man called Hoy, strange name, guess it's Orknadian, but you know what Dad's like, you can't take him anywhere without someone knowing him.

Night All - love Lula x
(and of course Love from Dad x)

Saturday 30/11/19

Not too early a start today, though early enough
to watch and wait for the sunrise.

It's a cracking morning, it's great just sat
watching for the first proper glint of the sun.

Big news this morning

We were watching the sunrise and Eddie tried to sneak across the yard to go to work, got him no problem – made sure he was clean and tidy, gave his ears a proper going over.

Guess What ? Big News!

Eddie has changed his name overnight by deed poll to **Arthur** how cool is that.

Unless of course Dad had his name wrong in the first place – can't imagine that though TBH – Roflmao (*memory like a sieve Dad at times*).

Anyway **Arthur** had his wash, and I let him make a fuss of me like I enjoyed it – I think I've trapped – he's asked me again if I'll stay here when Dad goes home.

I've told him I'm thinking about it.

Right – Coffee's done, Arthur's done, and we're off to meet this old mate of Dad's called Hoy.

We've got to catch a ferry to another island – guess who's on ferry watch again.

We're off – it's a lovely day, the sea's like a mill pond according to Dad - whatever that is – *I think he sometimes forgets I'm a dog and I don't have a clue what he's talking about.*

64

We've arrived at the island and we're getting off the ferry.

Just look at the ferry front – *I know what a tuna feels like now inside a great white shark!*

The Old Man of Hoy

We're off the ferry, we've driven to a car park in the middle of nowhere surrounded by mountains.

Guess Dad's mate is late because there's no one else here.

Hmm – he's just broken the news that we've got to walk up a mountain (he's calling it a hill) to see this chap Hoy - *He'd better be worth it!*

Views on the way up are good though.

Must be getting close now surely!

Apparently not – we just keep going up!

This old man we're meeting must be fit for his age if he's up and down this mountain all the time.

I must admit though the views are stunning.

Well I can't get my breath !!!!!

No, it's not the altitude, or the climb.

This old man mate of Dad's isn't a man at all, it's a lump of rock called **The Old Man of Hoy** - its famous, supposedly – it's my fault for misunderstanding apparently.

I'll not be getting a fuss out of that then.

I've dragged my backside all the way up a mountain in the wind and rain just to look at a lump of rock - *I'm really not happy!*

Oh - and he tells me that we won't have time to go all the way to it if we want to get the last ferry home – *oh what a shame that is - I don't think!*

Staying with Arthur becomes more and more attractive!

Anyway here's as close as we are going to get – it's the little lump of rock stuck up to the left of the headland in the distance.

Ok – back to the car park, the ferry, the cottage, tea and bed.

Had to show you this one first – this is a picture of the mountain we had to climb from the car park.

We're in the ferry queue - I'm not sure if I'm having a power nap or recovering from the shock.

I know Dad's not quite right in the head some days, but he reckons we might come back here next week at a different time to see if we can get the whole way to the rock and back. Hoping he's just winding me up - if not then Arthur here I come.

Dad's got to go hunter gathering for tea.

That's not very Neolithic now is it.

We're home, I'm fed, watered, cuddled up, warm and sleepy.

Maybe Dad's not such a bad old stick after all, having second thoughts about Arthur's offer TBH.

Night all Love Lula xx
(and of course Love from Dad x)

Sunday 1/12/19

We're having a chilled day today, not going anywhere, just going to enjoy the cottage and a peaceful day.

Started off with another terrific sunrise.

We've chilled for long enough, as beautiful as the sunrise is I'm dragging the old man out for a walk, what he doesn't know is that the manure field smells lush this morning.

Can't wait.

Looks like we've set off in the dark – but it's not really, Dad wanted more pictures of the sun rising, looks dark because the cameras pointing at the sun. *If we'd waited until he'd sorted the camera settings out it would have been! LOL*

Good news and bad news:

Good news, these are better photo's facing away from the sun.

Bad news:

He's found a way down to the coast **without** crossing the manure field – what a bummer (pardon the pun), he says it'll save me having bad breath – *bit personal that I think*.

We're at the shore

The water is gin clear according to Dad whatever that means.

Anyway, I thought I'd have a quick crabbing session.

I don't want to bump into the brother of the one Dad ate the other day, although at least I'd be able to see it coming.

Spot of advanced free climbing next I think, overhangs, the works.

Dad said I couldn't do it – *Oh ye of little faith!*

I didn't bother summiting it was too easy – *Everest next I think!*

Oops! A little out of order this one – it was on the way down to the shore, these touch screen phones aren't designed for paws – Apple take note!

We're heading home – time for a drink and a sit.

Look who's here.

It's my best mate Arthur – he's fab, just sorting his ears out again on this one. Sorry it's not the best of pictures. Also whispering to him that his hat is better than Dad's – couldn't let Dad hear – you know how twitchy he is about his hat.

Competition time for all bloggers

What's this?

A few clues:

- We found it on the shore off Scapa Flow
- It's metal
- It's very rusty
- German War Ships

Best answer wins the object, my decision is final, answers asap please.

We're back at the cottage just in time, its lashing down.

Nice and cosy in the cottage though

Yep – this is what Sunday afternoons are all about, time for a quick dog nap I think. First though quick check of the 'pits' – he's had a shower but it's always worth a check.

No it wasn't the 'pits' LOL – I'm having a power nap.

Wide awake now – time for a Sunday afternoon snack.

Guess who's got what? - not quite sure why I keep losing out – Athurs' offer comes to mind again.

Well the rains gone but I've persuaded him to stay in – needed more chilling time LOL.

Arthur's been round and taken Dad to meet some visitors – he seemed very excited.

Oh No! Look who's been to see Arthur?

I'm gutted, they're lovely, not sure he'll still love me the best.

I'm heartbroken!

Feeling better now – snuggled up with Dad, nothing quite like it TBH, guess me and Arthur can still be friends – *Still think that I might ask for an Arthur for Xmas though – he's fab, bet he'd be a monkey to wrap though.*

Tea Time.

Hmmm! – I'm not very happy.

This is Dad's cheesecake – I **can't** have any.

He's also having a lamb stew and mashed potatoes – I **can't** have any.

Guess what I've got?

Yep – good old biscuits and water!!!

This is going to have to get sorted.

That lamb stew smelled fab, he even had mint sauce to go with it, I can't get my breath.

Oh Oh! – Massive apology needed

I ended up with the left over stew and gravy with my biscuits

Absolutely Lush !!!!!!!!!!!!

Stick a fork in me I'm done!

I'm stuffed now – I can't move, not sure I'll make it to bed.

He's not a bad Dad after all.

Night All – I need to get some kip, we're going to hunt the Northern Lights tomorrow so probably a late night.

Sleep tight everybody, sweet dreams, talk tomorrow
Love Lula xx

(and of course Love from Dad xx)

Sorry guys – late message from my niece Ivy.

Hi Lula

*Mum read your blog to me and to be honest I never get nice food!!! So I thought if you've had some of Grandad's stew I'd help myself to Mum's Sunday dinner ..... **She wasn't happy !!***

Hi Ivy

Oh dear – take a tip from an older woman – next time, wait until she's gone out of the room, wolf it down, then run to one of the kids and lick their fingers – she'll think they've had it, works every time babe – say nothing x

Message from big Sis Dani - *"Are you two losing the plot" LOL – hope it's not hereditary.*

I've messaged back:

"Sorry Babe - You've no chance" xx

One last message for tonight:

Katie please pass on.

Dear Ivy
So sorry I didn't include you before, I didn't
realise you'd cracked using the internet / phone
/ text yet as you're so young. I've added you
onto the bloggers list now with your mum -
make sure she keeps you up to date, I blog
every day - Keep Growling.

Love Lula xx

Oh dear just had a thought!

Ellen for goodness sake don't put this on U
Tube – if it goes viral we'll be on 'Strictly Come
Dancing' next. I don't mind the dancing, but the
sequins are a definite No No!

Ellen *: LOL*
Dani*: Put the wine away Dad LOL*
Ellen: *Roflmao*

Katie*: I think the sequins would suit you Lula,*
blue sparkly sequins, definitely your style.

Hi Katie – *Not me you pillock – Dad!*

Katie: *Oh no, definitely no sequins for Dad!*
Pink headbands are his limit!

Dad's rolling at that but to be honest I don't know why?

Katie: *I'll let Dad explain, all I'll say is when you're in public tomorrow ask Dad to wear your collar LOL*

Okey Dokey will do.

Night All Love Lula xx
(and of course Love from Dad x)

Monday 2/12/19

Hi Everybody.

Bit of a grey start this morning but it did brighten up a little after a while.

These are both the same place believe it or not.

I missed Arthur this morning, I think he's out there somewhere – you never can tell.

I've told Dad straight this morning - *I'm not going out in this – clown coat or not – it's not happening.*

Just look what he's done for my cheek – he's put me on 'weather watch'

I'm getting wrapped up it looks cold out there.

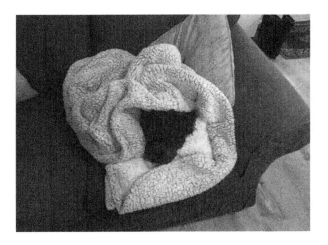

I've had a visit from Ann – she's got a poorly leg so has to kneel down so I can give her the once over, normal stuff – ears, neck, hands etc, she's fab, I think Arthur's passed on the soap saving idea TBH.

Weathers improved, though it's still not great –
I've let him know.

'Flippin Heck' we're still going out, he's not right in the head.

I'm **NOT** wearing that coat – in your dreams!

We're going fishing.

We've arrived.

It's a nice spot, Arthur's told Dad that there are lots of Sea Trout about.

Dad's chosen to go near the bridge – it's a pinch point apparently – *if he pinches me he'll be seeing a side of me he won't like!*

Ah – A pinch point is where two bits of land come close together, anything swimming up between the two shores will have to come through here and under the bridge – that's Dad's theory anyway.

We'll see how it goes, if he catches as much as normal we'll be having lamb stew for tea. LOL

Trouble Brewing !!!

Well we've arrived at the bridge. Dad's got his rod set up and been fishing for about 10 mins.

Out of the blue a local turns up – young chap, says his name is Cyril, he tells Dad in a not very friendly tone – 'You've nicked my fishing spot'.

Well you know Dad – if the lad had asked Dad to move, or said it in a nice way, Dad would have moved further along the bank but instead it ended up Dad telling him to do one! Cyril went off crying – saying he was fetching his Dad – Sam.

Dad said 'Whatever – bring it on' – Dad's a bit grumpy now – oh dear.

Sam and Cyril arrived back. Dad put me back in the car out of the way then stomped back to the fishing spot.

Sam and Cyril are really kicking off about fishing rights for locals etc etc. They're really not happy.

Dad's just carried on fishing away, they got really grumpy – sounded like they were hissing and snorting at Dad.

I shouted to Dad – 'Come on Dad we can take these', 'in hard and out fast', becoming a bit of a family motto that – they really drew me TBH – nobody talks to Dad like that – (wonder where I get that from then eh sisters).

Next thing another local - Harry, joined in – now its 3 vs 1.

Well, you know how you can tell when its coming from Dad when he gives out the "Paddington Bear Hard Stare".

Well, out it came.

I thought 'brace yourselves guys – incoming'.

Anyway it all got a bit heated, Harry did one – flew down the bank like his backside was on fire – Dad's really grumpy now.

Next thing Dad puts his rod down.

Squares up to them both and tells them to 'put up or shut up' and 'if you 2 Muppets don't disappear you'll be getting wet'.

At that the 2 of them scarpered.

(I've translated quite a lot of this, there were quite a lot of words Dad actually used that I don't think you would understand TBH – he must have picked up some Celtic from somewhere).

Best not to mess with Dad when he loses it!

I managed 1 photo though. This is Cyril – he's keeping his distance now, Sam's out there somewhere!

Cyril stayed to glare at Dad for a while – I'm thinking in your dreams pal – you'll have to get past me first.

Harry the heron was never seen again.

Dad carried on fishing for a while – guess what – he never caught a thing. He blamed the seals – *not so sure about that TBH*

Rains back – heading home to get dry and warm, and to enjoy a little snack.

Snack Time

Going to be giving out Paddington Bear Hard Stares myself any time now.

He's got scones and tea.

What have I got – yep dog biscuits yet again – I think he forgets I'm on holiday too.

Tea Time

We've had a little siesta and its tea time.

He's really winding me up now!

He's knocked up a cottage pie, put fruit on the cheesecake, and he's got scones in case he's still hungry – he's turning into a right little piggy wiggy, and oh joy – I've got the good old dog biscuits again – *whooppee!!! I don't think.*

I'm going on hunger strike !!!!!!

It just keeps getting better and better – look what's happened now.

Arthur's been round, and now Dad's got a pair of Lobsters for tea.

I can't believe it.

He's going to give them the same treatment as Crabby had the other night.

WHERE'S MINE !!!!!!!!!

Nope this is not happening – *I'm not eating that!!*

105

You've got fresh lobster **or** cottage pie, cheesecake and scones.

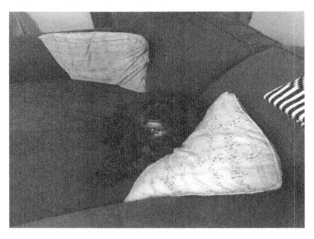

I'm asking for a transfer! - **Hunger Strike on in a big way!**

See untouched by canine paw.

Just Look! – Lobster, Soda Bread and Butter –
I can't believe it.

Samuel: Ha Ha.

*Katie / Ivy: Even I'm jealous Lula – at least he
took you with him.*

Hang on a minute

Faaabbbuuuullloouussss –

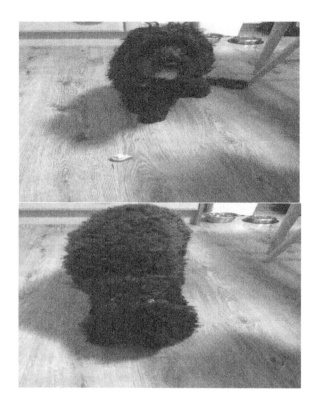

I've got a Lobster Canape – yummy!

Hunger strike over me thinks.

**Absolutely
LLLLLUUUUSSSSSSHHHHH!!!**

And I've even got the gravy that was meant for the pie with my biscuits – absolutely fab.

Good News – we're staying in, it's too cloudy and rainy to see the Northern Lights tonight.

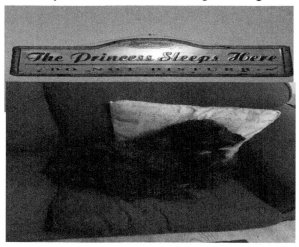

We're all good – loved the lobster starter, I could get used to that.

I'm set for the night now, it's warm, dry, and I'm full – just like a princess should be. Better still he's got the pots to do.

Night All.

Love Lula xx
(and of course Love from Dad x)

Tuesday 3/12/19

Hiya Bloggers.

Stop Press: The competition has been won.

Well done Samuel (nephew) the prize is yours – your answer was spot on, it's part of a warship scuttled by the German Navy when they surrendered to avoid the Royal Navy having the ships.

You can have the prize when we get home.

Ok on with the day.

It's a bit of a grim start – foggy or what!

No crabbing trip for us today.

It was blowing a gale last night – I got up for a wee and had to take Dad out with me in case I blew away – bit scary TBH.

Dad told Arthur this morning that I looked like Dumbo trying to take off – I'm guessing that's a compliment, it made Arthur smile.

Talk about grim weather – Brekkie's not much
better – What's happened to the Lobster?

Poor start to the day but the fog's blown away now, and I've had a visit from my new best mates.

That was good – both adopted parents around for their wash, Ann's great – easy peasy to get to when she sits down for me.

Arthur's looking good in his new hat.

I had a quiet word about the lack of lobster for brekkie this morning, he's asked me if I'm developing tastes I can't afford – we've not told him yet that I am actually a princess and should be treated accordingly.

Anyway, he's said he'll see what he can do.

We're going out – off for a look around. Dad has a couple of places he wants to go to, and if the weather holds up we're going to try and see the Northern Lights tonight.

Scapa Beach

Its dry but blowing like crazy, nice beach though, just having a look around.

I've rated this beach a "double pooper" for obvious reasons I think – good job Dad's got a few bags with him LOL, I think from now on I'll give each place a "pooper" rating – you never know it might catch on.

Just having a check to make sure of the rating

Yep – Defo "double pooper" beach.

Time for a walk on the sand.

I've made a new friend – not very lively, but lovely to roll on, he was wearing lovely aftershave.

Not according to Dad - *he's threatened me with a shower – oops!*

I've left my new friend where he was, just laying catching the rays, he wasn't very chirpy anyway TBH.

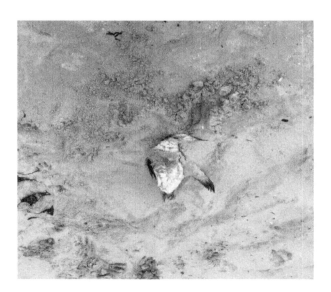

Look at this place for a guest house – doesn't look very welcoming does it – *talk about prepare to 'repel boarders'.*

Dad said it might be for those that don't pay their bill.

Give me Feawell, and Arthur and Ann everyday of the week.

Next stop – a special place called **Highland Park** – it's not a very good park, I wasn't allowed in, I couldn't see a blade of grass anywhere.

Dad nipped in and seemed much happier when he came out – I don't know why though.

Another special place apparently – **Orkney Brewery** - I wasn't allowed in again but I did get a nice whiff of something from somewhere.

There's a bit of a story to the next picture. We stopped in the middle of nowhere to take a picture of the mountains in the sunset – it didn't come out very well so I've not included it, but this memorial just happened to be where we pulled in. It's important - it commemorates people serving here in the war – it's great it's here but it ought to be more obvious - we could have driven past it without even knowing it – that would have been very sad.

Heading back home for tea now, Dad's gone hunter gathering again

I'm pretty sure this isn't the way it was in Neolithic times.

We've arrived home and I'm not very happy —
Crabby 2 has arrived.

Is there nothing out there for me?

I've had a word with Arthur and he's promised
me he'll sort something out - **Good Old Arthur.**

The weather's improving – lovely sky, Dad's just told me we're going out tonight to see the **Northern Lights** if we can – Double Dutch to me tbh, we're in the North, it's light already, what more is there – still it's Gilbert to humour him if it keeps him happy.

'Gilbert' – who's Gilbert?

It should have said 'best to humour him' – that's predictive text for you.

I'll have to get my nails cut it might help with the typing – Apple haven't come back to me yet with my earlier request to design around paw use – think I'll try a Samsung next.

Time for a quick power nap – I've made him lay still for a while- we're out late, and he needs his beauty sleep – (**more than most TBH**), a shave wouldn't go amiss either – He just says "I'm on holiday – do one".

(Sisters joining in)

Katie / Ivy
*On form with the blogs today Lula – Have a
nice nap xx*

Daniella
*I'd love to be cuddled up on that sofa -we were
out late drinking 70% vodka in Poland and
now on the way to the airport xx*

Nap over.

We're dining out – we're taking a picnic.

This is his -

He's got - Crab and Lobster in a lemon, oil, and vinegar dressing with salt and pepper, sour dough bread and butter, cheesecake with fresh assorted berries and cream, mince pies, worlds best caramel wafers, fresh fruit, coffee, and beer.

It's like living with blinking Marco Pierre White – we must be staying in the only Michelin 2 star self catering cottage in Orkney.

And what have I got?

I'm really, really on one now.

He's winding me up good and proper- I swear to god he's going to get it good style next time I get in the manure field.

Ah ok – he's gathered I'm sulking, the situations improved, these are my beefy chews, still doesn't quite cut the biscuit though.

Look, I'm at it now – we've all gone food crazy, **"Doesn't quite cut the biscuit"** - where did that come from?

I've never seen any biscuits that need cutting.

Come on Dad let's get off – sooner we're there the sooner we can start the picnic.

We're off – we're going to **Birsay Island**, there were some photo's earlier in the blog in day light, its pitch black outside so we'll not get any new ones, it's about half an hour drive, I'll check back in when we're there.

Birsay Island
The Hunt for the Northern Lights

We've arrived, it's pitch black outside, the stars are out, and we just sit and wait until somebody turns a switch on and lights appear in the sky, this is my kind of hobby, Easy Peasy lemon squeezy.

I'm on right window watch – nothing as yet.

Katie and Ivy: *sent 4 'crying with laughter' imoji.*

He's got me on left window watch now, its making my neck ache all this moving from one side to the other.

Hang On - What a laugh - He's only left the 2 Michelin Star picnic back at the cottage. **Roflmao!** I nearly wet myself when he realised, Oh God my sides ache, I can't breathe !!!!!!!!!!

Katie and Ivy: *sent 5 Crying with Laughter imoji.*

There's always a down side –

OMG! just realised that means he's not brought my chews either – that's not so funny

– What a plonker!

He's blaming me now, for running off to find Arthur when we left – thought it might be my fault somehow!

I thought this was a nice picture TBH – got my best side I think. I know it looks like he's nearly asleep but it was the flash on the camera – it made him blink.

It's not a problem - when Apple sort out a paw friendly phone I'll crop his head out of the photo – he'll never know.

Beaten to it !!!

Look what he's done now – I'm all warm and cuddled up, I've dropped off for 5 mins, and my heads lolled back, it looks like he's cut **my** head off before I could do it to him.

He's such a smart Alec at times.

Home time

Come on Dad we've been here for ages – I think the money's run out in the meter for the lights.

Let's try again tomorrow.

Besides, that picnic and those chews aren't

going to eat themselves.

You did cook Crabby 2 didn't you? If he gets in that box he'll be having my chews

Come on Dad – lets be going.

Message received from niece

Ivy: *I tried to help you find those Northern Light things Grandad has you looking for, they aren't here either, sorry !!!*

Mum wasn't very happy though – told me to get down, I was only trying to help! (crying imoji)

Daniella: *Maybe she's looking for the men in white coats coming to pick you up!!!!!!!*

Hiya Ivy

Great! Thanks for the help, really appreciate it, if you spot anything just let me know.

Anything will do just to make him happy - a white bird, a bit of coloured paper, milk bottle top - anything to be honest - his eyes aren't good enough to know the difference LOL.

Don't worry about your mum - she's like a chip off the old block (Oh god - there goes the food reference again – he's doing my head in with all this cooking).

Hi Dani *As long as they've got torches he'll be happy with that.*

Ok folks – we're home, dry, warm and safe.

Night All – Love Lula xx
(and of course Love from Dad xxx)

Wednesday 4/12/19

Hiya Bloggers.

Overcast, wild and woolly this morning - nice though.

No crabbing trip with Arthur – it's too rough apparently – and he should know – he's a

skipper on a supply boat out on the proper seas in his spare time. What a hero and look how well trained he is – he's even hanging out the washing – we have to get an Arthur for home!!!!

You'd better double peg them Arch if you want them to be there until they're dry!

Just look at this – they have some strange ways in Orkney, they hang their washing out horizontally, it'll never catch on down South.

They even grow their plants in a strange way – the grassy thing next to the washing pole grows at right angles to the floor.

Then again it maybe because the wind's blowing at 1000mph!!!!!!

Text from big sis Ell: *This is all very funny.*

Just having a quick look at the weather – it's blowing a hoolley – hopefully we're not going far in this.

The washing won't take long to dry in this Arch!!

Look he's fetched it in already – it's better than having a tumble dryer living up here! lol.

O.M.G !!!!!!!!!!!

I've had a visit from Arthur – he's not only done the washing this morning he's also got me a pressie.

Dad's had Crabby 1 and Crabby 2, and the lobsters.

Look what Arthur and Ann have got me?

a **FISHY !!!!!**

Yeah! A **whole** fishy just for me – Arthur and Ann are awesome – bit like a living version of Ken and Barbie but better looking and much more fun.

Come on Marco let's see what you can make of this!

Good News and Bad News

Good News:

I've decided what to do with Fishy - Marco's on it

Bad News: He's looking at it and thinking "This would make a cracking fish pie".

Marco – Step Away from the Fishy!!!!!!

Hmmm – slavering now, sorry not too pretty I know.

We (**Me** and **Marco**) discussed what to make – Cod Mornay, Cod Souffle, Cod in Cheese sauce, the list went on and on..... . In the end I decided on just good old plain Cod.

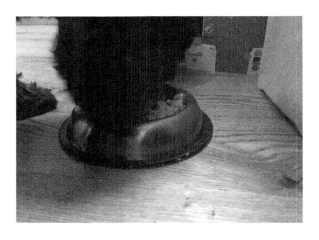

"YUMMMMMY"
(I can't get my head far enough into this
bowl !!!) Job done – even managed
to avoid the biscuits he 'd snuck into the mix.

**He'll have to get up a bit earlier in the day
to catch me out!**

I'm stuffed and really need a siesta. **Looks like I've got a little food baby in the next picture LOL.**

Right I'm having 5 – Stick a fork in me I'm done.

Arthur and Ann: I love you x

And there's even some left for tomorrow, this really is doggy heaven

Ivy you'll have to come next time, but you'll have to behave yourself when you meet Arthur and Ann – otherwise we'll be falling out.

Dad's Poorly!

We've had a run out, we've been to a place called Scapa Distillery, I couldn't go in – adults only I'm told.

I came to the conclusion that it's a health farm.

Dad came back with a box and a strange smell on his breath, he said "Keep your paws off that – it's mine, and for medicinal purposes only" - I guess he's not very well, but this seemed to do him good.

Called back here for some reason – **Highland Park.** Dad came back holding something under his coat – "medicinal purposes again" he said.

Starting to worry about Dad – I didn't realise he was that ill.

We've called back at the fishing spot. Dad got his rod out and we headed towards the shore – a big furry thing with a white tail ran away like mad – **guess Dad's rep has got around.**

Got to the spot, would you believe it - Sam and Cyril we're sunbathing on the shore, they soon scarpered when they saw Dad.

Dad started fishing then Sam and Cyril's whole family turned up, there must have been 5 or 6 of them, Dad tried to get a picture of all of them together, for identikit reasons I guess, in case they decided to have a go.

They stayed well away, probably wisest given what he's done to crabby 1 and 2, and Larry and Leonard the lobsters this week.

Cyril tried to give us the Paddington Bear Hard Stare routine – he doesn't know he's up against experts in that game - "Bring it on Cyril – Does this face looked bothered!"

(best photo I could find of my 'does this face looked bothered" face LOL).

Dad fished for a while then we turned around and noticed this.

It's a big storm blowing in.

Dad's been told that it's going to be that bad tonight and tomorrow that the ferries may be cancelled.

God forbid that we've got to stay here after Friday surviving on Crab, Lobster and Fishy - what a nightmare that would be LOL.

We've returned home – its lashing down with rain, he's not good enough with the camera to get a photo of it but TBH even the Clown coat seems a decent option if we go out in this!

We're all good – we're staying in – no clown coat required.

He's turned back into Marco again – he's thinking what he can make with this lot -

To be honest I really **don't** care, I know I have Fishy in the fridge for tomorrow- better make sure he doesn't think about a fish pie.

MARCO – I'VE TOLD YOU BEFORE – STAY AWAY FROM THE FRIDGE !!!!!!!!!

This is my tea - standard biscuits - but I'm ok with that today. Fishy tomorrow from my beloved Arthur – he's a dreamboat – very apt that considering he's a proper fisherman and skipper – **He can sail my boat any time!**

A quick check outside – it's like the black hole. of Calcutta, and blowing an absolute gale.

Glad we're tucked up warm and cosy.

Embarrassing or what!

Not too happy with the next photo.

He's caught me sorting out my intimate bits –
he's no sense of decorum whatsoever – **Dani,
you need to have a word when we get home.**

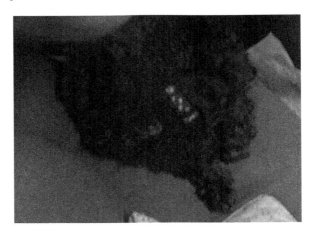

Teas up from Marco.

Apparently it's a version of a Fritatta, that's a
posh word for an omelette type thingy with
loads of stuff in it.

This one has sweet potato, baby corn,
tomatoes, wilted lettuce, lobster, and grated
mixed cheese (Cheddar and Emmental), with a
garlic mayonnaise dip on the side.

Sounds a lot of fuss to me, he's just using up leftovers, the tight git – bring on my fishy tomorrow.

I've decided Dad's right - Cod is the best fish in the world – especially when it's all for **me**.

Daniella: *That tea sounds very nice !! Dad can whip that up for both me and you Lula when you're both home.*

Right – I'm getting my head down, it's been a tiring old day, still blowing a gale outside, but it's warm and cosy in here.

Night All – fishy dreams (I know I will) – back on the blog tomorrow.

Love Lula xx
(And of course Love from Dad xx)
(Guess he deserves a mention, the fishy was fab – just what a princess like me deserves – LOL)

Daniella: *"Also Lula please don't scare off the local inhabitants, sharing is key if you want to go back there xx"*

P.S. Forgot to mention – he's not kissing me tomorrow, second hand garlic mayo – **I don't think so!**

What a cheek he has to have a go about my manure breath – hmph!!!!.

Nighty Night.
Love Lula xx
(and of course Love from Dad x)

PPS Hiya Dani – *I know what you mean but we've been talking to Amazing Arthur today and there's a pod of Orca that visit Scapa Flow. They make a real mess of the seals, so I guess grumpy Dad is a bit of a wuss by comparison.*

PPPS Dani – *sorry sis you asked about penguins, sorry babe but you're geography is rubbish TBH - they only live in the southern hemisphere.*

I found a puffin though – Nice chap very quiet, but cute none the less.

Meet Peter the Puffin, he's a resident here at the cottage, he's very quiet, doesn't make a mess, and doesn't seem to eat a lot.

Just been for a wee and I've seen my first shooting star – how cool is that, too quick to take a photo, but great none the less.

Dan*i: I think you should get Peter a friend when you're out and about so he's not lonely when you leave x*

What do you suggest?

Dani *- "Another Puffin !!!!!"*

Okey Dokey we'll have a look for one.

Night All.

Love Lula xx
(and of course love from Dad xx)

Thursday 5/12/19

Hiya Bloggers.

Big day on Orkney today, headlines for tomorrow's papers:

Orkney in Turmoil – Grand Theft, Murder, and Canine Cruelty – Ferries cancelled until Culprits found.

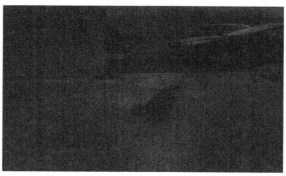

What a start to the day – we've got up, normal time, everything good, went outside and guess what – someone's stolen the Sun! Look it's gone.

I've headed back in for a cuddle with Dad.

Arthur and Ann came round to play – great.

Dad got a bit of a telling off from Arthur – apparently the smell from my fishy cooking drove their cats wild yesterday - hee hee hee.

Little do they know there's some in the fridge for later today.

Dad – keep that front door closed – I'm going back on fishy watch!

Somebodies turned a light on somewhere but still no sun – wouldn't think the robber would be hard to find though – there can't be many people on Orkney today wearing factor 50 and sunglasses.

Its light enough for us to go out – so we're off.

Scail Bay

First visit of the day Scail Bay.

Waves are higher than a house, it doesn't look it on the piccies but trust me the wind is blowing an absolute gale and the sea is crashing in.

Time for a beach comb – come on Dad get your finger out – it's this way.

OMG – Help , Police, Murder !!!!!

I think its Cyril from the other day – or what's left of him, I can't tell because his top half is missing!

Dad – you wouldn't would you? No it can't be Dad, he hasn't been out of my sight all day, probably Odin the 'Orrible Orca – him and his mates are around here somewhere.

I tried to revive Cyril by giving him a cardiac massage rub with my neck – I knew all the practice on fox poo would come in handy.

Sadly to no avail – Cyril is no longer with us.

163

Time to head back – Cyril Rest in Piece.

(wonder who'll spot the deliberate play on words there – very canny for a canine eh!)

Hang on a minute – it doesn't show on the piccie but there's a chap out there on the horizon – there's only me and Dad looney enough to be out today – this guy can't be up to any good - it could be the sun thief.

Oi you – have you got the Sun?

He says not – he's got the Mirror.

Fat lot of good that'll do him, no point brushing your hair in this lot.

Look the winds got stronger and the sea higher. Look at the next piccies of the headland – the seas crashing right over the cliffs – brilliant.

Dad I don't care if it'd make a good photo – I'm not going in the sea in this lot and that's final, and absolutely **no** bikini shots – you must be raving mad – tell you what you go in and I'll stand in the dry taking the pictures for a change - *That's told him - the looney !*

Can I taste the salt – I can almost see it!

Time to move on – we're going to **Marwick Bay** next.

Marwick Bay

We're on the straightest road in the world – you can see right down it and straight into the sea.

Literally straight into the sea.

Slow down a bit Dad – we don't want to get wet.

Will you slow down – it's getting closer!

Well how clever was that – we've stopped about 6 ft from the sea – he was nearly having to use a poo bag **before** we got out of the car.

Look – this Idiot didn't stop in time now did he – told you it was dangerous!

Marwick Bay proper photo's – the sea was really crashing in, the waves are higher than a house, it's blowing an absolute gale.

The little blob on the top of the hill is where we're going next.

Bit of a rubbish photo – he's had to stick two together and couldn't quite make them match!

Kitchener's Monument

Just doing a little bit of sun spotting on the way – no luck I'm afraid.

Its blowing a gale, lashing down with rain, we're going having to walk up to this thing on the hill – can't wait – **I don't think**.

Contemplating the Clown coat TBH – **that's** how bad it is.

Well we're in the car park, he's made his mind up we're going to have a closer look – it's a million miles away and on top of the mountain – it's the little blob at the top of the first picture.

Time to go up.

We're getting there but it's still a long way – it must be massive.

Well they can say that again!

LOL – he's forgot my lead, I walked all the way up here without it, but he doesn't want me chasing the bunnies that are all over the place up here – shame it might have made a nice alternative to fishy.

Don't think we can go to the monument now – the only way is along the cliffs and he doesn't want me off a lead – it's not safe to let me run around.

We got here – its brilliant, great views and a superb monument to Kitchener and the men that died with him in the war.

178

But how did I get here without my lead?

- Did he carry me? **No**
- Did we find a safe, dry, out of the hurricane wind and torrential rain route across the cliff tops? **No**

Of course not – we're talking about Dad here. he's made me wear his **BELT** – just look, **how embarrassing is this!!!!**

It's a good job there's only us mad enough to be out in this – I could have died when he did that.

And to top it all he wanted to plonk me on top of that wall pillar to get a better photo, *I flatly refused that – He doesn't pay me enough.*

Last couple of pictures as we head back to the car.

LOL though – his super waterproof, wind proof, cold proof trousers don't work on his right leg in Orkney, his leg's wet,

Welcome to my world Daddyo - I'VE GOT 4 OF THEM.

We're back in the car like a pair of drowned rats, at least it's not windy in here.

I'm back on sun spotting again - living in a false hope there I'm afraid – **just look at my hair!!**

The picture isn't very interesting other than it's at this point he tells me I'm heading for a shower when we get back.

Cyril has left a reminder with me, and I stink supposedly – what's Dad expect – the poor little chap couldn't exactly say "Bye" now could he – he didn't have a head!

Canine Cruelty

We've arrived home – first thing for me – **a shower, !!!!**

Now I ask you if this isn't canine cruelty what is?

Just look – he's made a bigger mess of my hair
than the rain and wind did.

For god's sake!!

I look like flipping Crystal Tips now – I'm going nowhere looking like this.

Come on Dad – I need food – comfort eating required in a big way!

Ahhh Fishy – Fanks Dad xxxx

That's it folks - I'm a bit on the fluffy side, but I'm warm, dry, and full of fishy.

Nighty Night.

Love from Lula xx
(and of course love from Dad xx)

oh ps – Forgot to mention Amazing Arthur has asked me to stay again. He's promised to give up the sailor's life and stay home to look after me.

What do you think?

He's also offered Dad a job – him and Ann had some of Dads cheesecake, he wants Dad to be a cook on board his ship.

The cook he has does fish and mushy peas which no one eats, then turns the peas into pea soup the following day – which no one eats, then the next night adds spices and fish and calls it a Thai Green Curry – I thought he might make a fortune selling the recipes to Weightwatchers LOL

Amazing Arthur isn't too impressed by that – especially after tasting Dads cheesecake.

Dani texted: *I'm glad you've had a wash Lula, you've been looking too much like a wild dog lately from the pics. I feel bad for Cyril, if the Orcas appear stay away, as for you both staying there are you forgetting about us at home???xxx*

No Dani – but I'm thinking if it works out you could come and live next door, I think I could twist Arthur's arm to supply fishy as part of the deal. I'll not see Odin the Orca if I don't stay with Arthur and Ann, I'm on a ferry tomorrow heading back with Dad. I've promised Arthur and Ann an answer first thing in the morning.

Text from Ivy: *Hi Lula – sorry for the delay, I was just settling the kids down ready for bed, they like a story to chill out.*

It looks crazy out there Lula, poor Cyril - I know you two didn't always see eye to eye but you

wouldn't wish that on anyone.

Love Ivy X

My feelings exactly Ivy, that's why I tried to revive him. It is difficult to bear a grudge against someone who's had their head bitten off to be honest.

Ivy sent: *Good on you Lula, you should have been getting an extra portion of 'fishy' today for the sheer courage and bravery you've shown, not a shower and a blow dry!*
#unappreciated
#Arthurwouldnttakeyouforgranted

Hmmm more food for thought – thanks for the input Ivy.

Ivy: Don't tell Grandad (I saw what you said about Crabby), but I can't stop having a little chuckle about his wet right leg (LOL) – I imagine he wasn't too happy about that one.

Your secrets safe with me Ivy, I chuckled into the head rest myself TBH. He's got a vicious side too him – especially when he walks and you can hear his right leg splashing about.

Ivy sent: *Ha Ha, I think its karma Lula for making you wear the clown coat.*

What goes around comes around babe that's what I always say.

That's it for today gang.

Night all Love Lula xx
(and of course love from Dad xx)

Friday 6/12/19 – Decision Day

Hi Guys.

Big day today – I have to decide whether to stay with Arthur and Ann or come home with Dad.

TBH I've not slept for most of the night and had to have a long heart to heart with Dad – he's quite good at that you know.

Arthur's called round, it's really early, it's still dark – guess he couldn't sleep either.

He came in the dark – I think he didn't want me to see him cry if I said no.

I think I've broken his heart.

We had a good talk, I told him that as much as I love him and Ann I've decided to go home with Dad.

He's gone off now to be on his own on his fishing boat – it was horrible seeing a grown man cry – coming around in the dark didn't work.

I've told him we can stay in touch, and that him and Ann will always have a special place in my heart, and that they are both fabulous, he was so upset but I think it's for the best in the long run.

Just checking if Arthur's back yet, I thought I heard him, I hope he's ok.

Nope - he's not back yet**Roflmao**

Just look at this.

We were packing and I said 'Dad – quick it's the Northern Lights - you can see it through the door'. He dashed and got his phone and took the picture!!!

What a plonker – it's the reflection of the room light in the door glass.

Whatever you do don't let on – he's been like a cat that's had the cream all day –you got to feel sorry for him tbh.

I'm on the lookout for Arthur and his boat – I think I can see it but only just, guess he's throwing himself into his work to get over it.

YAY I can see him, you probably can't this camera is rubbish,

I'll have to see if Dad's due for an upgrade.

Hope Arthur's coming to terms with me leaving him, I think he is - I'm both happy and sad at the same time TBH.

Any Fishy left for Brekkie Dad?

Hmph – Apparently not!!! I ate all the fishy yesterday, this is all I've got, and will have in the future.

I knew there'd be a major downside!!

Dad's packing

Oddly enough he seems to be taking a lot more back with him than he came with.

His big bag looked ever so heavy when he heaved it into the car.

No wonder it's heavy – he's had it away with the top half of every mountain in Orkney, and the sunrise – this is the same view we've had all week but this time there are no mountains and no sun!

Everybody likes a memento but this is ridiculous – we'll never get this lot on the ferry.

Sorry to say Goodbye – it's time to start for home I'm absolutely torn – want to stay but also can't not go home with Dad.

We're all packed, Ann came round for one last visit, no doubt Arthur's told her my decision but she's put on a brave face and never mentioned it – she's such a lady – I **love** Ann.

Anyway she had a good read of the blog - laughed a lot,

I was a little worried when she told Dad **"***Don't worry about calling Arthur "Eddie" - he's always had a split personality anyway"***- Lucky escape maybe**.

We had a good cuddle and said our goodbyes, that was a sad moment, but I've promised I'll see her again, she's lovely xx – sad to say it's time to leave Feawell.

Long Way to go

We're heading to the ferry – Dad says I need to settle down we've got a long drive today, heading West along the North coast of Scotland and then down the East coast to Ullapool.

Last few piccies of Orkney.

These are for you Sam Bam - they're some of
the scuttled ships in the sea.

Oh and don't worry – I checked your prize it's in the back of the car.

We're back at the ferry.

Bye Bye Orkney – it's been Fab!

Two thoughts keep running through my mind.

How's Arhur ?

And - I'm convinced this chair will give me piles.

We've come inside out of the wind and rain – I'm still thinking about Arthur – I can't see his fishy boat anywhere.

Do you think he's ok Dad ?

Just having a quiet moment. I'm sure he'll be alright, not sure I will be though.

Hello Scotland – Och Aye the Noo !

That's what they say up here, I've no idea what it means but hey ho when in Rome ....

We're on the road – long way to go but some nice views ahead I'm told.

He'll not be taking many piccies as he's driving.

This one isn't great but that's Dunnett Head in the distance – and that **is** the most Northerly point of the UK mainland

First comfort break, beautiful piccie (the countryside isn't bad either LOL).

Gorgeous but t's time to head into the mountains

You've got to admire his consistency – we're close to the top of the world and he's still found somewhere to fish.

Told you we were near the top of the world —
these are clouds we're driving into, hope he's
brought the Oxygen cylinder, though looking at
the state of this car he'll never find it.

We're on the way down, went a little giddy there
for a while. **What a laugh**, when I type **'giddy'**
predictive text puts **'fishy'** - I'm starting to like
this phone.

The Vikings have landed

We'd been driving downhill for a while and stopped for another comfort break.

It was near a place called Smoo Cave,

Vikings were here,

I asked Dad why 'Smoo', he said it's because Vikings wore hats with horns growing out of the side like a cow.

Guess it should have been called s**MOO** cave, unless Dad's just being a smart Alec again of course.

Worst photograph ever taken by anyone ever

It's gone dark now, we're driving down the side of a mountain and in the lights there are 2 deer grazing at the side of the road, they were beautiful. Dad says "if we see any more we'll get a photo".

A little further on 2 stags are grazing, stags are deer with Antlers on their heads – that's all I can tell you, we slowed down, but it took him that long to check mirror, signal, check mirror, manoeuvre, stop, engage handbrake, put car in neutral, pick up the phone, put in the pass code, open up photo's, and take the picture, they'd had time for a tea party, a massage, a sauna, pay the bill, and dawdle off into the dark before he hit the button, it was brilliant – I was wetting myself.

Here's the photo – brilliant isn't it LOL.

We saw a quite a few more deer after these TBH but we never slowed down - **not a word was said** – roflmao! (in silence of course)

Ullapool

It's been a long drive, we've arrived in Ullapool. Its pitch black so no outside photo's as yet but here's the new pad, it's nice, but not quite as comfy as Arthur and Ann's.

Still a little upset about leaving Arthur though, I don't really fancy food.

He's sneaky is Dad, he's mixed some of his Cornish pasty and gravy in with my biscuits – can't resist – Lush! - Sorry Arthur but a girl's got to eat.

215

I'm stuffed, warm, and snuggled up – I still love Arthur and Ann but I think I'll be ok.

Night All love Lula xx
(and of course Love from Dad x)

Hold the front page!

O.M.G – **Arthur still loves me**.

Look at the e mail he's sent Dad.

*"Hi Martyn – you didn't say you were going fishing or I'd have come with you, just sitting down to our fish and chips, **Give love to Lola** – Arthur"*.
I know it says **Lola**, but it was a predictive text problem. Arthur has as much trouble with techy things as Dad (I know that's hard to believe but it's true).

He's still my hero and I still love him and Ann – I'm so glad he's ok, I'll sleep much better tonight now.

Night Night All – loads of love Lula
(and of course Love from Dad xx)

Dani: *Oh Lula I know you're sad to be leaving your new friends but I can't wait to see you on Monday!!!! The deer looked like they were enjoying their tea party to be fair, hope the next stop is more comfy, and ask Dad if he can bring me something tasty back from Scotland xx*

Any clues on the something tasty Dani? - they don't do vegetarian haggis

Dani: *Biscuits would be nice – Reece has eaten all of mine xx*

Okey dokey - I'll see what I can do.

Katie*: Sending lots of love Lula, it was a hard decision to make but for what it's worth I think you've made the right one, he (Dad) can be a bit of a grump, but Arthur has nothing on Dad xx*

Thanks Katie -

Night All – Love Lula xx
(and of course love from Dad xx)

Saturday 7/12/19

Hiya Gang – it's blog time.

Just a quickie from last night though.

Got up for a wee – bit early to be honest, around 5.00ish,

Dad wasn't too happy.

Anyway thought I'd cheer him up with a game of hide and seek in the dark. (Actually I'd snuck off for a number 2 in private – you need privacy for that don't you, he always closes the door when he goes).

Didn't go down as well as planned TBH – the hide and seek I mean.

He was stomping about in bare feet in his pj's in the rain, but to be honest I couldn't go straight back, well once you've started you've got to finish haven't you, bit like Mastermind – he was really not happy in a big way.

Went back into the room and there's a light in the distance, I told him "I bet that's the Northern Lights, take a picture".

Actually it's the port of Ullapool but you wouldn't know from the blob in the picture – he really really needs an upgrade.

We went back to bed for a while and got up to this view.

It was fab — and kept getting better and better the lighter it got, it was dark when we arrived so we'd not seen anything.

Except that is for the lovely lady who met us, showed us where we were staying and gave Dad some milk for a cup of tea.

She also told us that deer often come down to the forest edge behind the cottages in the mornings.

They weren't here this morning so we're going to go and look for them before we set off.

Deer Hunting

After yesterday's disaster photo I think he's decided that there's no way we're leaving Scotland without a picture of a deer, and I get the feeling that it's up to me to do the finding, so we're off on a yomp through the forest to see what we can see.

Takes me back to bear hunting with Samuel TBH – but that's a story for another day.

We've made a start.

I've picked up the scent – Come on Dad follow me.

We're getting closer.

Look a handbag they've dropped, I know it's a deers' - it says "Antler" on it.

Tell you what, you stay there and I'll hide behind this twig – they'll never spot us.

What's that over there?

Look, a fresh hoof print – nearly got them.

Got Him – Sometimes I forget just how good I am TBH – **LOL so proud of myself it hurts!**

On the Road

We're off – roads are a little tricky so not many photo's, we're heading to Fort William via Loch Ness and more hunting for a lady called

Nessie.

We've driven the whole length of this Loch

there's absolutely no sign of Nessie.

No - I'm not going any further – you just want to take a picture of the splash when I drop in – **Do one!!**

Tell you what Dad – see if we can borrow this – we'd have more of a chance.

He's losing his touch – we couldn't borrow it, there's no sign of Nessie, and I've not seen any fishy either.

We'll ask a few locals if they know where Nessie is.

"Hi Ladies – anyone here called Nessie?"

"Ayup Duck – Have you seen Nessie?"

No Luck – no one knows where she is.

Time to go to **Fort William** and a look at **Ben Nevis** – Dad's hoping to see snow on top, he'll be lucky if there's any top left with all this rain.

We've arrived – It was a nice trip with nice scenery but it's lashing down with rain here.

I was right, Ben Nevis used to be there in the background, it's gone! Washed away in all this rain.

We're like a pair of drowned rats - and we've been in the car most of the day – it's ruined my blow wave.

ALL RIGHT !– stop going on.

You were right, I was wrong.

Next time I'll wear the flipping clown coat.

BACK OFF WITH THAT HAIR DRYER!!

We've had better views as well to be honest.

Good News and Bad News

Good News:

We're staying in, it's lashing down outside, Dads having a takeaway and I'm having my biscuits then we're settling down, big day tomorrow apparently.

Bad News

He's brought the guitar in!

Think I'll play dead – he might take pity on me.

Playing dead worked – the guitar has stayed in the case - hoorah!

He's had an Indian, I've had my biscuits, been for a wee and had a good rub down, – we're settling down for the night – warm, dryish, and comfy.

Night All.

Love from Lula
(and of course love from Dad x)

Dani - *"I never found Nessie either Lula, I commend you for your efforts though, shame you and Dad couldn't borrow the submarine"*

Sunday 8/12/19

Hiya Bloggers.

Start of an epic day I think.

We're up early – it's still dark – **Does this man ever sleep?**

This is the view from the front of last night's kennel – better than the view from the room window but not exactly what we're used to.

Can you believe it we're going for a look around the shops, the world is still in bed and we're going shopping!

It's lashing down with rain, I'm going to get wet through (**again**) and we're going shopping.

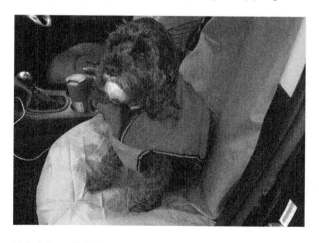

Wishing I'd kept my mouth shut TBH.

Look how busy it is (*not*) – well we'll not get killed in the rush!

I'm going to keep to the edge – less conspicuous that way.

Just look at this:

Dad – look its deserted, all the shops are shut – let's go back to bed eh?

Come on what do you think?

Ah - apparently it's the best time to come shopping because you can't buy anything! **Tight or What !!!!!**

I've taken a photo of a deer for him, I think it might be a reindeer TBH but as he hasn't got a photo to compare it too he'll never know – LOL

Here you are Dani – there's a penguin or two
hiding in these pictures maybe you were right
all along,

I've found Nessie too.

There's no wonder we couldn't find any of these before
– it's out of season and they've all come here to Fort William for a holiday.

At least there's one chap out and about.

Come on Dad I've blagged us a lift back.

Just to formally announce that there is a God, and he looks after all creatures, especially me.

Thank you God - the shop is **closed,** and why's that important ????

I'm absolutely not, repeat **NOT** wearing that, never mind that it goes with the clown coat – **I'll feed myself to Nessie first!!!**

Here Dad – this the closest you'll ever get to a Stag - LOL

My God – look where we're going next Dad buy me that hat I might need it!

Oh that was smart – he's taken a picture of a picture very funny – not!

This chap's been here all night, I bet he's frozen.

Shall I talk to him Dad?

"Ayup Mate – Och Aye the Noo. How are you doing?"

He **must** be frozen.- **He's giving me the cold shoulder!**

Mystery Tour

We've packed, loaded the car up, driven for 2 minutes and boarded a train.

It's not very busy, I can't say where we're going, it's a surprise for Dani.

We've been going a while and I'm dying to tell Dani where we're headed.

Oh and by the way that isn't Dad's handbag and newspaper on the table, it's on the opposite side of the carriage. I thought I should explain about the **newspaper**, don't want you all dying of shock.

C'mon Dad let's tell her.

Hmmph! Spoilsport.

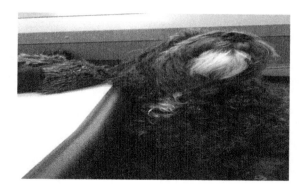

Aww! Come on Dad the suspense is killing me.

Looks like we're going to give you clues.

These are some of the stations on the way to our destination.

Quick clue break

Meet Tony the Ticket Collector - **"Ticket please Ma'am"**.

He was lovely, he had to have the once over, (glad Arthur's not seeing this – I think he might have a jealous streak)

Views from the line

These were just some of the views - they were stunning, the piccies don't do them justice, the fact that it was lashing down with rain and the glass was covered in rain drops spoilt the photo's.

Ok – it's time to see why we've done this train ride

Not the best of pictures but hope you can see.

It's the viaduct the **Hogwarts Express** takes in the **Harry Potter** films, the train goes from Fort William to Mallag.

The views are stunning, these are as we passed over the viaduct.

After the viaduct the train climbs high into the mountains, the views are incredible, here's a few – we could fill albums and albums of photo's – best bet would be to go yourself – it's worth the trip.

If you time it right you can catch **the actual Hogwarts Express** – unfortunately it was in the maintenance shed when we were here.

Mallag

Great journey – we've arrived at Mallag.

Bye Tony thanks for the ride – how lucky are you to have a job that brings you up here every day.

"Oo Arr Jim Lad"

Hang on, who's nicked my wooden leg?

Right Dad – that's seen Mallag, it's nice little town but really cold, windy and rainy – the train back isn't for 2 hours – what's next?

Ah – the pub watching the snooker – **very dog friendly that is!**

I take it all back, it's a lovely place in here, this pub gets my recommendation.

That's all from Mallag and the Hogwarts Line, its back on the train to Fort William and a long drive to Carlisle in the rain and dark.

One last picture though – these are my first train tickets – I think I'll stick them above my food bowl at home as a reminder. (Wonder where I got that idea from eh Dani?)

Fort William to Carlisle

I've no doubt that in Summer, Spring, or Winter proper (if the snow allowed) this would be a really enjoyable beautifully scenic drive.

Tonight in the dark, pelting rain, and hurricane strength winds it was horrendous.

We've driven for 5 hours in the dark. through hurricane like winds, up and over mountains on roads that were goat tracks (or felt like it).
Up, down, and across roads that had turned into rivers, and around car crashes that were probably caused by so much rain that the drivers couldn't see.

I had a few 'sharp intake of breath' moments, a few 'squeeze in Dad – phew we made it moments', and a few moments where I thought Dad was going to have to find my poo bags to be honest.

But we made it in the end safe and sound – Well Done Dad!

I've had tea, I'm warm, cozy and settling down.

Dad's earned what he's got.

Though where he magicked that and the corkscrew from I'll never know.

Right folks that's it for today.

Night All – Love from Lula x
(and of course love from Dad x)

Monday 9/12/2019
The Return

Early morning text from Dani: *Wow! He must have made you get up early to fit all that in yesterday! Very jealous about the Hogwarts trip – glad you didn't meet any dementors!!*

Me and Reece are looking forward to seeing you both later xx

Hiya Bloggers.

It's the last blog today, how sad is that, and where have the last 2 weeks gone.

Any way following a very dodgy drive last night and blogging 'til the early hours this was the view from our window this morning.

Not good I grant you but TBH I've blogged worse.

Last night's kennel was ok, and I had a good rub from both of the receptionists, that always lifts the feedback scores up a few notches.

Any way not many piccies today, it's a strange day- I'm happy(ish) to be heading home, thinking about the great times I've had over the last few weeks, so a mixture of happy and sad at the same time.

We've set off

The motorways ok but after 20 mins I've already seen more cars than I saw in the whole 2 weeks in Orkney.

TBH I've a niggle in the back of my mind that I can't quite put my paw on.

Having a good chat with Dad in the car – we're trying to decide our top 3 highlights from the holiday, it's very difficult to be honest.

We've eaten loads of things

- Fishy (that gets my vote into the top 3)
- Lobster (that gets Dad's vote as a top 3)
- Crab (that gets both mine and Dad's vote as a top 3 - LOL)

We probably need a top 10

We've done loads of things:

- Fishing, walking, crabbing, car rides, train rides, boat rides.
- Visited ancient sites.
- Made new friends, and new enemies – Sam, Cyril, and Harry (not really – they were only doing what's natural to them).
- Held a competition – (Well done Sam Bam).
- Met local wildlife – Cyril, Sam and Harry.
- Looked for the Northern Lights that never appeared..........

The list goes on and on, it's all been great.

We're stopping in Stockport for a comfort break and a coffee.

(Still got that niggle in my mind).

Sorry guys not very exciting this, we're both a bit glum.

We're back in the car – still thinking about the holiday.

We've done exactly 1653 miles over the last 14 days not including trains or ferries, or walking – which felt like another 2000 LOL.

- Got wet through, cold, and tired.

- Got dry, warm, and slept like the dead – (felt good then about going out and getting wet through, cold, and tired – **how odd is that!**).
- Found dead bodies on beaches.
- Done extreme sports: free
- climbing, crabbing **(yes it is extreme – especially when there are Orca about),** orienteering up mountains in hurricanes.
- Cooked and ate the locals.
- Photography – some good some bad (*remember the Deer LOL*)

And above all else simply **chilled.**

We've arrived back home, emptied the car and had it cleaned
(God it was a mess, we never did find the oxygen cylinder LOL).

Text from Ell (Big Sis):

I loved reading the blog, shame it's come to an end.

Yay – Dani's Home.

Hiya Sis – Give us a kiss

…….. and a hug

She thinks I've lost weight – it's all the exercise – walking, climbing, crabbing, and healthy eating, Arthur's fishy was superb, his Lobster and crabby even better – Lllluuussshhhhh !!!!!!

I still have that niggle though.

Text from Katie / Ivy: *Gonna miss the blog Lula.*

It was a long drive back home and me and Dad talked a lot about what we'd done and seen, and as far as the top three are concerned we've decided one thing is definite.

We came to Orkney originally with just one thing in mind - would we be lucky enough to see the Northern Lights?

Text from Katie and Ivy: *What's the niggle Lula?*

Well we never did, but we found Orkney, its history, its geography, its people, and the chilled way of life absolutely fantastic, and whilst we didn't find the lights we did find two stars.

Yep - Ann and Arthur.

I know I've said it before but me and Dad think they are brilliant.

It's not just the cosy, spotlessly clean, warm, comfortable cottage, but Ann and Arthur themselves, nothing is too much trouble, they love a laugh, and as far as we're concerned they can do no wrong.

So who actually needs the lights when you have 2 Northern Stars to see and even better – these two come out in the day as well!

I've still got that niggle though!

Ahh – I know what it is – it's Dad, - he reminds me of somebody.

Now who is it?

The guy from Assassins Creed?

No – not even close.

Peter Barlow maybe?

'Maybe' is the word – '**Maybe**' 25 years ago LOL.

We'll have to work this out.

Who is it?

It's on the tip of my tongue.

Let me think.

Grey Beard, Black Coat - Who is it ??????

I've got an idea - come on Dad put this on.

I think we're nearly there – any ideas anybody?

Text from Katie: *No idea – I'm intrigued though - A Russian Spy?*

I've an idea.

Right Dad – put this on, it's the missing piece of the jigsaw, it'll be perfect.

What do you mean **NO**!!

Now look. I've had to:

- Wear a Clown Coat
- A Belt
- Have photo's published of me sorting my bits out
- Photo's of me straight out of the shower,
- Photo's of me looking like Crystal Tips after a blow dry
- Slavering over Fishy etc etc

In your dreams if you think you're avoiding this.

Get this on!!!

Absolutely Perfect.

So who does Dad remind me of ....

IT'S ME!!!

Look at those ears, the little grey beard, the frilly
fringe, glossy black coat, and shiny black nose,
it's me to a T – he's brill my Dad.

They do say that over time owners and their
dogs grow to look like each other – I think this
holiday has had a good effect on him.

**Hopefully not me – I really don't want those
wrinkles – LOL**

Ellen: *"I was going to say that LOL"*

Katie: *(7 smiley faces) - "Right that's it now, this has gone too far! Ladies we need a quick trip to the local mental unit – He's actually lost it!"*

Ellen: *"Yep, think it's time."*

Katie: *"What must the person taking the picture have thought???????"*

Ellen: *"That was my next question LOL "*

There we go folks Lula's blog finishes today. Thanks for reading and responding, it's been a great way of letting you know about our holiday. In all honesty it was **superb,** Arthur and Ann are absolute stars, if anyone wants to stay in a great little cottage on Orkney then Feawell Cottage with Ann and Arthur is the place.

For all of the great things we've seen and places we've been, the memories of early morning chats on the doorstep of the cottage with Arthur and Ann, cup of tea in hand, watching the sun rise over the hills to reflect in the bay, are the ones that return first, last longest, and will bring us back to this very special place.

Night All - Loads of love from Lula x (and of course Love from Dad x)

Lula's Blog Over and Out.

Printed in Great Britain
by Amazon